FIREMAN SAM'S

ABC

Illustrated by The County Studio

HEINEMANN·LONDON

First published in Great Britain 1991
by William Heinemann Young Books
an imprint of Reed International Books Limited
Michelin House, 81 Fulham Road, London SW3 6RB and Auckland
Reprinted 1998
Fireman Sam copyright © 1985 Prism Art & Design Limited
Text copyright © 1991 Reed International Books Limited
Illustrations copyright © 1991 Reed International Books Limited
All rights reserved
Based on the animation series produced by
Bumper Films for S4C – Channel 4 Wales –
and Prism Art & Design Limited
Original idea by Dave Gingell and Dave Jones,
assisted by Mike Young
Characters created by Rob Lee

ISBN 0 434 97356 4

A CIP record of this book is available
at the British library.

Printed in Hong Kong

A a   alarm

The alarm rings when there is a fire.

B b boots

Fireman Sam and Elvis wear black boots.

C c cafe

Bella and Rosa live at the cafe.

D d Dilys

Dilys works in her shop.

E e Elvis

Elvis enjoys cooking for everyone.

F f fire station

Jupiter waits at the fire station.

G g glasses

Norman and Bella wear glasses.

Hh hose

Fireman Sam uses the hose.

Ii ink

Norman spills ink on his book.

Jj Jupiter

Fireman Sam uses Jupiter every day.

K k kite

Penny helps James to fly his kite.

L l ladder

Elvis climbs up the ladder to rescue Rosa.

Mm message

Fireman Sam reads the message.

N n Norman

Naughty Norman likes to play tricks!

O o orange

James and Sarah are buying oranges.

P p Pontypandy

The fire brigade of Pontypandy.

Q q quarry

Penny climbs down the quarry
to rescue James.

R r Rosa

Rosa is Bella's cat.

S s Station Officer Steele

Station Officer Steele is in charge.

Tt telephone

Trevor hears the telephone ring.

Uu uncle

Fireman Sam is James's and Sarah's uncle.

V v Venus

Venus is Penny's rescue tender.

W w water

Fireman Sam uses lots of water.

X x e<u>x</u>tinguisher

Penny points the extinguisher at the flames.

Y y yawn

What a big yawn, Trevor!

Z z zip

The zip is broken.